a gift for us to share

to: . . . .

from: . . . .

OTHER HELEN EXLEY®LONDON BOOKS IN THIS SERIES:
Me and my Mum
Me and my Grandma
Me and my Grandad

OTHER HELEN EXLEY® LONDON:
365 For My Dad
To the greatest Dad ever
To a very special Dad

ISBN 978-1-78485-083-8

10   9   8   7   6   5   4   3   2   1

Printed in Turkey.

LONDON

Helen Exley Gifts,
16 Chalk Hill, Watford,
Herts WD19 4BG, UK.
www.helenexley.com

Written by Helen Exley and Illustrated by Jane Massey

Me
and my
Dad

This is my Dad. We often sit together. He loves it when I'm not being a total menace. Most of all, my Dad is proud of me. He says so.

My Dad swings me round and round and round.

I laugh and laugh.

I laugh so much
when he makes me fly.

It's the very happiest I can be.

My Dad's very strong,
but he's also gentle.
Once I found a bird with
a broken wing and he looked
after it until it could fly.
He's kind to me, too.

Dad and I cook together.
He's in charge of the stove and
makes smoke and smells,

and I'm in charge

of the mixing bowl.

Daddy sometimes falls asleep when he reads me my bedtime stories. It's because I love the same ones over and over and over again.
I think it tires him out.

Daddy showed me how to swim.

"I won't let you go, I promise,"
he said, as he held me.

From then onwards I felt safe.

My Dad's good at fixing things in the house, but sometimes he hits his thumb instead of the nail. Then it's my special job to make it better and mend him.

My Dad always has lots of bills to pay and a long list of jobs to do. But sometimes he just wants to put his poor old feet up. One day he taught me his best Dad-word -mañana, which he says means, "I'll do it tomorrow!"

I feel so lonely when my Dad
has to go far away with his work.
Sometimes I think Daddy cries too,
because he loves me so much.

My Dad grumbles when I make
the worst mess ever.
He always says,
"It's total chaos".

And then he smiles
and says,
"Never mind."
And we pick
it all up.

My Daddy helps me with my homework. He tries very hard. (But my teacher doesn't think much of his spelling.)

For my party Dad blew up all the balloons, even when nearly all his puff was gone!

Good old Dad

-isn't he the best!

WHAT IS A HELEN EXLEY GIFTBOOK?

Helen Exley has been creating Gift Books for forty years,
and her readers have bought more than 141 million copies
of her works in forty five languages.
Because her books are bought as gifts, she makes sure
that each book is as thoughtful and meaningful a gift
as it is possible to create: good to give, good to receive.

You have the result in your hands.
If you have found it valuable - tell others!